THE BEATLES TRIVIA BOOK

Uncover The History Of One Of The
Greatest Bands To Ever Walk This Earth!

By Dale Raynes

Please consider writing a review!

Just visit: purplelink.org/review

Bridge Press.

bp@purplelink.org

ISBN: 978-1-955149-11-2

TABLE OF CONTENTS

INTRODUCTION

Widely regarded as the most famous band in music history, The Beatles are a household name known around the world. Offering themes and images of peace, love, self-discovery, and togetherness, The Beatles have built an everlasting fandom inspired by their music, creativity, and timeless relatability.

The Beatles dominated the international music scene for more than half of the 1960s, appealing to the youth and reflecting the social movements of the time. Their music has reached audiences of every generation for the past several decades. To help you connect—or perhaps reconnect—with the lives, music, and legacy of the band, this book covers interesting facts and highlights historical moments.

The Beatles Trivia Book covers the backstories and influences of The Beatles beginning with the origins of the band up to their status today. A series of multiple choice and true or false questions open each chapter with the corresponding answers on the following page. A "Did You Know" portion consisting of interesting facts and stories closes each chapter so that you can round out that topic with a stronger connection to the life and music of The Beatles.

The information and statistics in this book are up to date as of early 2021. Because the band's peak years have come and gone, the historical facts should remain mostly consistent. While the surviving two members continue to be musically active, the band has ceased any new activity in April 1970 and officially dissolved in 1975. The only exception was a collaboration on the Beatles Anthology series in the mid-1990s. Records and stats may fluctuate with future anniversary releases.

Use this book to test your knowledge with a round of trivia on various topics and perhaps review or gain new knowledge along the way. Whether you consider yourself a die-hard fan or are only faintly familiar with The Beatles, this book offers the opportunity to reinforce your knowledge of one of the most important bands in the history of popular music.

Let's see how much you know about The Beatles!

CHAPTER 1:

HISTORY AND ORIGINS

TRIVIA TIME!

1. In which British city was The Beatles initially formed?

   a. London
   b. Liverpool
   c. Manchester
   d. Glasgow

2. What was the name of John Lennon's skiffle band that Paul McCartney joined in 1957, followed by George Harrison in 1958?

   a. The Quarrymen
   b. Johnny and the Boys
   c. Britband
   d. Buddy Holly and the Crickets

3. True or False: The Beatles were the most photographed subject of the 1960s.

4. True or False: The haircuts of the members of the band were iconic and caused their own worldwide sensation.

5. Which city in Germany was the host of The Beatles' periodic residencies in their early years?

   a. Berlin
   b. Hamburg
   c. Frankfurt
   d. Leipzig

6. True or False: Only Paul McCartney and John Lennon contributed vocals to their albums.

7. True or False: The founding members of The Beatles were teenagers at the time the band formed.

8. The Beatles' UK popularity notably started at which venue in Liverpool?

   a. Eric's Club
   b. The Concert Square
   c. The Cavern Club
   d. The Zanzibar Club

9. As their popularity grew, what nickname did the principal group of four Beatles acquire?

   a. The Fab Four
   b. The Fantastic Four
   c. The Four Horsemen
   d. The Four Friends

10. True or False: All of The Beatles could read sheet music.

11. True or False: The original lineup of The Beatles was four members.

12. The mass fanaticism and media frenzy provoked by The Beatles when they rose to international stardom in the 1960s is referred to as what?

a. Beatle Invasion
b. Flying Beatles
c. Beatlemania
d. Peace, Love, Beatles

13. In what year did The Beatles arrive in America at the John F. Kennedy International Airport in New York?

a. 1960
b. 1964
c. 1966
d. 1970

14. True or False: The idea for the name The Beatles was inspired by the name of the band Buddy Holly and The Crickets.

15. True or False: The Beatles were all multi-instrumentalists.

16. Which studio in London hosted the most recordings created by The Beatles?

a. Britannia Row Studios
b. Trident Studio
c. Abbey Road Studios
d. RGM Sound

17. The Beatles were part of a cultural phenomenon involving multiple rock and pop groups from the UK becoming popular in the US. What was this musical movement was called?

a. The Rad Rocker Rave
b. The English Takeover
c. The Boy Band Frenzy
d. The British Invasion

18. True or False: Because of civil rights issues in the US, The Beatles had to play at segregated shows.

19. What was the location of The Beatles' first live performance in the US?

    a. The Washington Coliseum
    b. Madison Square Garden
    c. Carnegie Hall
    d. Radio City Music Hall

20. What was the name of the newspaper publication in Liverpool that carried early stories and photos of The Beatles, along with other local bands and stars from the early 1960s?

    a. The Independent
    b. Mersey Beat
    c. Liverpool Echo
    d. Band Beats

ANSWERS

1. b — Liverpool

2. a — The Quarrymen

3. True

4. True

5. b — Hamburg

6. False

7. True

8. c — The Cavern Club

9. a — The Fab Four

10. False

11. False

12. c — Beatlemania

13. b — 1964

14. True

15. True

16. c — Abbey Road Studios

17. d — The British Invasion

18. False

19. a — The Washington Coliseum

20. b — Mersey Beat

DID YOU KNOW?

- On July 6, 1957, John Lennon and Paul McCartney met for the first time at St. Peter's Church in Liverpool, England, where John's skiffle band The Quarrymen was performing. McCartney joined The Quarrymen, which would later become The Beatles in 1960.

- The name "The Beatles" was derived from a play on the words "beat" and "beetles." The insect element is rumored to have been inspired by Buddy Holly and the Crickets.

- The Liverpool publication *Mersey Beat* printed news about the local bands and stars performing in Merseyside County in the early 1960s. In 1962, they held a poll to determine the most popular group, and The Beatles won, of course!

- During their residency in Hamburg and early performances in Liverpool, The Beatles often donned black all-leather outfits, a staple in German fashion.

- The Beatles' UK popularity started with their performances at The Cavern Club. The Quarrymen made their first appearance at the club on August 7, 1957. They first performed there as the Beatles after returning to Liverpool from a residency in Hamburg.

- Two nights after arriving in the US for the first time, The Beatles played their first American concert at The Washington Coliseum in Washington D.C. Despite the coliseum owner, Harry Lynn, only running one ad in the Washington Post, the concert sold out in days.

- The press adopted the term "Beatlemania" in response to the scenes of hysteria and high-pitched screaming that characterized any appearance of The Beatles during their peak years. In 1977, a musical of the same name premiered on Broadway, highlighting the history of the 1960's through the music of the Beatles.

- During their US tour in 1964, The Beatles were scheduled to perform in a segregated venue at Jacksonville's Gator Bowl, in Florida. They refused to perform unless the audience was integrated and included clauses in their contracts that stipulated all of their shows be integrated in subsequent tours.

- The mass hysteria and safety concerns at their live performances, coupled with inadequate sound equipment, caused The Beatles to halt live performances in 1966, ending four years of non-stop touring. They continued recording music in the studio, where they took advantage of the use of studio technology.

- The Beatles were mostly self-taught musicians who had never learned to read music. At first, The Beatles were mostly a guitar and drum band, but over the years the group became accomplished multi-instrumentalists.

- While Paul McCartney's first instrument was the piano, the first that he personally owned was a nickel-plated trumpet, given to him by his father. However, when rock and roll became popular, he traded this instrument for a fifteen-pound Framus Zenith, a common steel-string acoustic guitar.

- Both Paul McCartney and George Harrison were inspired by Slim Whitman's guitar playing. For Paul, this inspiration came in the form of the idea to switch his strings around and he began playing left-handed. George, however, simply had not seen others play the guitar before Slim Whitman.

- At first, John Lennon felt that at 14, George Harrison was too young to join the group. But when Paul McCartney arranged a meeting, young George managed to impress John by performing the lead guitar part from the instrumental "Raunchy."

CHAPTER 2:

KEY PEOPLE

TRIVIA TIME!

1. Partnered with John Lennon, which other Beatle was jointly credited for most of The Beatles music?
   a. Ringo Starr
   b. Paul McCartney
   c. Brian Wilson
   d. Eric Clapton
2. Which Beatle was considered the lead guitarist and sometimes called "the quiet Beatle"?
   a. John Lennon
   b. Jimi Hendrix
   c. George Harrison
   d. Pete Best
3. Back in their early years in Hamburg and Liverpool, who was The Beatles' manager?
   a. Paul McCartney
   b. Allan Williams
   c. Brian Epstein
   d. Allen Klein

4. True or False: Harrison, McCartney, and Lennon all played guitar.

5. What is drummer Ringo Starr's birth name?

   a. Bo Stark
   b. Richard Starkey
   c. Ray Stern
   d. Ron Strum

6. Who was The Beatles' most trusted manager, who helped bring them into the mainstream spotlight?

   a. Allen Klein
   b. Michael Jackson
   c. Murray Wilson
   d. Brian Epstein

7. George Harrison was best friends with which famous guitarist of the band Cream?

   a. Mick Jagger
   b. Eddie Van Halen
   c. Eric Clapton
   d. Chuck Berry

8. Who was called "The Beatles' Guru" after The Beatles began studying the Transcendental Meditation Technique he invented?

   a. Sri Sri Ravi Shankar
   b. Tirumalai Krishnamacharya
   c. Krishna Pattabhi Jois
   d. Maharishi Mahesh Yogi

9. What was the name of the original bass player for The

Beatles, who John Lennon convinced to join from art school?

a. Stuart Sutcliffe
b. Martin Scott
c. Pete Best
d. Paul McCartney

10. After arranging their residency in Hamburg, who did The Beatles hire to be their first official drummer in 1960?

a. George Harrison
b. Miles Davis
c. Pete Best
d. Stuart Sutcliffe

11. True or False: The Beatles never used session musicians.

12. What was the name of the producer who signed The Beatles and recorded them for the first time at Abbey Road Studios?

a. Jack Mavis
b. George Martin
c. Phil Spector
d. Quincy Jones

13. Who was the soul musician from Houston, Texas that played electric piano and organ for The Beatles in 1969 and performed with the band at their final live performance that year?

a. Billy Preston
b. Ray Charles
c. Elton John
d. David Bowie

14. Who is the famous multimedia artist whom John Lennon

met at the Indica Gallery, London in 1966, and then married in 1969?

a. May Pang
b. Yayoi Kusama
c. Yoko Ono
d. Cynthia Lennon

15. During their early days in Hamburg, who was the German photographer that captured photos of the original members?

a. Ursula Andres
b. Anita Auspurg
c. Astrid Kirchherr
d. Marlene Dietrich

16. Which road manager started in 1963, contributed to many of The Beatles' recordings, and even appeared in most of their films?

a. Tony Barrow
b. Mal Evans
c. Geoff Emerick
d. Tommy Moore

17. Who was the publicist for The Beatles that coined the term, the "Fab Four" while promoting the band?

a. Brian Epstein
b. Albert Grossman
c. Tony Barrow
d. Barry Pepper

18. What was the name of the recording engineer at EMI Studios who worked with The Beatles from 1966-1969 and contributed greatly to their innovative and nontraditional

recording techniques?

a. Tom Scholz
b. Tom Meek
c. George Massenberg
d. Geoff Emerick

19. What was the name of John Lennon's fellow student at the Liverpool College of Art who started the *Mersey Beat*, a newspaper in the early 1960s that covered the Liverpool music scene?

a. Tommy Moore
b. Bill Harry
c. Ken Scott
d. Jimmie Nichol

20. True or False: Bob Dylan was a member of The Beatles for one year.

ANSWERS

1. b — Paul McCartney

2. c — George Harrison

3. b — Allan Williams

4. True

5. b — Richard Starkey

6. d — Brian Epstein

7. c — Eric Clapton

8. d — Maharishi Mahesh Yogi

9. a — Stuart Sutcliffe

10. c — Pete Best

11. False

12. b — George Martin

13. a — Billy Preston

14. c — Yoko Ono

15. c — Astrid Kirchherr

16. b — Mal Evans

17. c — Tony Barrow

18. d — Geoff Emerick

19. b — Bill Harry

20. False

DID YOU KNOW?

- John Lennon attended the Liverpool College of Art in 1957, where he met Stuart Sutcliffe and invited him to join The Beatles, although they were using a different band name at the time. In 1961, Sutcliffe left the band to continue pursuing painting, and sadly passed away in 1962 of a cerebral hemorrhage.

- "The Fifth Beatle" was an informal title given to various people who were either a member at one point or strongly associated with the band. Manager Brian Epstein, former drummer Pete Best, former bassist Stuart Sutcliffe, producer George Martin, and musician Billy Preston have all held the title due to their close involvement with The Beatles.

- Eric Clapton was close with The Beatles and recorded for them as a band as well as for each member on their solo albums. Clapton's closest Beatle buddy was fellow guitarist George Harrison.

- The Beatles rarely used session musicians since all of them were more than proficient on several instruments. In the first half of their career especially, they rarely used an extra musician outside of their producer, George Martin, who would occasionally record on keyboard instruments. Later into the 1960s, they started to include orchestral instruments and additional vocalists in some of their music.

- Astrid Kirchherr is known for her photographs of The Beatles from their time in Hamburg. She was a professional photographer and fan of The Beatles. She was also engaged to Stuart Sutcliffe before his death in 1962. She is often credited for their famous "mop-top" haircuts and giving the band their image at the time.

- Yoko Ono met John Lennon in London in 1966. She continued to pursue him until he left his first wife Cynthia a few years later. Lennon even changed his middle name to Ono, but because of British law had to also keep his middle name given at birth. His full name is John Winston Ono Lennon.

CHAPTER 3:

CHANGES TO THE BAND

TRIVIA TIME!

1. Which of the following was a short-lived name of the band before establishing the name "The Beatles"?

    a. The Black Beatles
    b. The Poison Beatles
    c. The Up-Beatles
    d. The Silver Beatles

2. At the encouragement of their manager Brian Epstein, The Beatles traded the leather jackets from their Hamburg days for which kind of attire moving forward?

    a. Suits and ties
    b. Trench coats
    c. Jean jackets
    d. Top hats

3. What year did The Beatles completely stop touring due to concerns about safety, exhaustion, and inadequate sound equipment?

a. 1969

b. 1968

c. 1967

d. 1966

4. As they evolved, The Beatles' albums began to feature the use of orchestral strings, a trend that started with which hit song?

a. "A Day in the Life"

b. "Yesterday"

c. "Eleanor Rigby"

d. "I Am the Walrus"

5. True or False: Paul McCartney covered on bass guitar after Sutcliffe left the band in 1961.

6. John Lennon started wearing his iconic round "granny" glasses in which year?

a. 1965

b. 1966

c. 1967

d. 1968

7. For which instrument did The Beatles have issues with recruiting and keeping a player in their early career?

a. Vocals

b. Bass

c. Guitar

d. Drums

8. Harrison's interest in meditation and Indian culture inspired him to take lessons and learn to play which

Indian string instrument?

a. Sitar
b. Violin
c. Sarod
d. Tambura

9. The iconic mop-top was a staple of The Beatles' image when they first gained worldwide stardom. What facial hair addition appeared on all four Beatles on the cover of *Sgt. Pepper's Lonely Hearts Club Band*?

a. Beard
b. Moustache
c. Goatee
d. Mutton chops

10. True or False: The Beatles incorporated Hindu-inspired spirituality and non-Western instruments into their music.

11. What is the name of the multimedia corporation founded by The Beatles that served as a creative and business venture for the group?

a. Apple Corps
b. Brother Beatles Corps
c. Give Peace Corps
d. Honey Tea Corps

12. True or False: The Beatles grew out their mop-tops for shaggy locks in the late 1960s.

13. In which year did The Beatles' beloved manager Brian Epstein pass away, signifying what most consider "the beginning of the end" for the band?

a. 1966

b. 1967

c. 1968

d. 1969

14. True or False: George Harrison wrote songs for The Beatles as he became a more avid songwriter in the mid to late 1960s.

15. True or False: The Beatles wrote mature music from the beginning, full of philosophical meaning and transcendent themes.

16. After much dispute and circulation of rumors, in which year did the media announce that The Beatles officially split (although it wouldn't be legal for another few years)?

a. 1968

b. 1969

c. 1970

d. 1971

17. While there were several things that contributed to the end of The Beatles, who is often blamed as the person who caused the split (although it is far more complicated and the accusation has repeatedly been denied)?

a. George Martin

b. Yoko Ono

c. Linda McCartney

d. Michael Jackson

18. True or False: Although The Beatles were rooted in skiffle and rock and roll, they evolved their music over time and even indirectly pioneered several genres of music.

ANSWERS

1. d — The Silver Beatles

2. a — Suits and ties

3. d — 1966

4. b — "Yesterday"

5. True

6. b — 1966

7. d — Drums

8. a — Sitar

9. b — Moustache

10. True

11. a — Apple Corps

12. True

13. b — 1967

14. True

15. False

16. c — 1970

17. b — Yoko Ono

18. True

DID YOU KNOW?

- On the eve of their first Hamburg stint in 1960, The Beatles recruited drummer Pete Best, and he became part of the original lineup of five along with John Lennon, Paul McCartney, George Harrison, Stuart Sutcliffe, and Pete Best. This changed soon after when Stuart Sutcliffe left the band in 1961 to resume his art studies in Germany, and Pete Best was replaced by Ringo Starr in 1962, when the band first recorded for George Martin at Abbey Road Studios. Although Pete Best had come before him, Ringo Starr became the "Fourth Beatle."

- The genre, style, and themes of the music of The Beatles continuously transformed with each new release. Their initial sound was rooted in the skiffle style, a type of folk music with jazz and blues flavors, in their incarnation as The Quarrymen. This quickly evolved into 1950s rock and roll and expanded to include pop in the 1960s.

- The lyrics of their formative years were full of themes of love and girls, but as they evolved as a band, so did their songwriting. Throughout the 1960s, The Beatles explored new musical territories and expanded the boundaries of rock and roll with influences of folk, country, psychedelia, classical, pop, and Indian music. Their lyrics adapted more mature themes such as philosophy, transcendence, self-awareness, and relationships. It was during this era of their music that they became leaders of peace activism, equality, and the anti-war movement.

- Into the late 1960s, the band started to splinter due to friction between the members. Many historians consider the untimely death of Brian Epstein in 1967 to be the turning point for The Beatles, since he often resolved their disputes and served as a strong leader.

- Harrison was growing as a songwriter but was met with rejection from Lennon and McCartney, which resulted in his alienation from the group. John Lennon privately informed his bandmates that he was leaving in 1969, but it was kept quiet from the media at the time due to the forthcoming album. In 1970, McCartney publicly announced his departure from The Beatles and moved to dissolve their contractual partnership. Each Beatle went on to continue recording solo music that met with success.

CHAPTER 4:

ALBUMS AND RECORD DEALS

TRIVIA TIME!

1. What was the name of the German-British record label that first signed The Beatles when they were recording as a backup band?

   a. Parlophone
   b. Decca Records
   c. Polydor Records
   d. Impression Recordings

2. Which record company famously rejected The Beatles, telling their manager, "Guitar groups are on their way out, Mr. Epstein"?

   a. Parlophone
   b. Decca Records
   c. Polydor Records
   d. EMI Records

3. The self-titled album *The Beatles* was given which nickname because of the color of its cover?

   a. *The Black Album*

b. *The White Album*

c. *The Blue Album*

d. *The Red Album*

4. George Martin was the producer for which record label when he signed The Beatles at Abbey Road Studios in 1962?

    a. Polydor Records

    b. Parlophone

    c. Apple Records

    d. Decca Records

5. The Beatles' debut album, mostly recorded in a single 13-hour session, was which of the following?

    a. *With the Beatles*

    b. *Beatles for Sale*

    c. *A Hard Day's Night*

    d. *Please Please Me*

6. Following their debut album, which Beatles LP sold half a million copies in one week, knocking its predecessor off the top of the charts?

    a. *With the Beatles*

    b. *Beatles for Sale*

    c. *A Hard Day's Night*

    d. *Please Please Me*

7. Which of The Beatles' albums was the first to be entirely written by Lennon and McCartney?

    a. *Revolver*

    b. *Rubber Soul*

    c. *With the Beatles*

    d. *A Hard Day's Night*

8. Establishing this trend for future artists, which Beatles album was the first rock album to include the lyrics on the cover sleeve?

    a. *Yellow Submarine*
    b. *Sgt. Pepper's Lonely Hearts Club Band*
    c. *The Beatles*
    d. *Abbey Road*

9. Under Vee-Jay Records, which was the first Beatles studio album to be released in the US, 10 days before Capitol's album release?

    a. *Introducing… The Beatles!*
    b. *With the Beatles*
    c. *Meet the Beatles!*
    d. *Beatles for Sale*

10. True or False: EMI Studios in London changed its name to Abbey Road Studios because of the success of the album of the same name.

11. Although not the last album to be recorded, which was the last album released by The Beatles in 1970?

    a. Abbey Road
    b. Sgt. Pepper's Lonely Hearts Club Band
    c. Let It Be
    d. The Beatles

12. Which Beatles album cover is the one of the most famous and frequently imitated images in popular music?

    a. *Revolver*
    b. *Abbey Road*
    c. *Let It Be*
    d. *Sgt. Pepper's Lonely Hearts Club Band*

13. True or False: The Beatles' album *Revolver* took over 700 hours to record.

14. Which album featured a distinctive sleeve design created by Klaus Voorman, a friend from The Beatles' days in Hamburg?

    a. *Revolver*
    b. *Sgt. Pepper's Lonely Hearts Club Band*
    c. *Rubber Soul*
    d. *Magical Mystery Tour*

15. As George Harrison became interested in Indian music and culture, he debuted his sitar playing on which album in 1965?

    a. *Help!*
    b. *Yellow Submarine*
    c. *Let It Be*
    d. *Rubber Soul*

16. Which Beatles album was the soundtrack for an animated feature film of the same name?

    a. *Yellow Submarine*
    b. *Magical Mystery Tour*
    c. *The Beatles*
    d. *Please Please Me*

17. Because the band was at odds, who did The Beatles bring in to piece together the album *Let It Be*?

    a. Johnny Cash
    b. Phil Spector
    c. Quincy Jones
    d. Eric Clapton

18. True or False: All of The Beatles albums only featured their original music and songs.

19. The Beatles are positioned in a flag semaphore of four letters on the cover of which album?

    a. *Yellow Submarine*
    b. *Rubber Soul*
    c. *Help!*
    d. *Sgt. Pepper's Lonely Hearts Club Band*

ANSWERS

1. c — Polydor Records

2. b — Decca Records

3. b — *The White Album*

4. b — Parlophone

5. d — *Please Please Me*

6. a — *With the Beatles*

7. d — *A Hard Day's Night*

8. b — *Sgt. Pepper's Lonely Hearts Club Band*

9. a — *Introducing… The Beatles!*

10. True

11. c — *Let It Be*

12. d — *Sgt. Pepper's Lonely Hearts Club Band*

13. False

14. a — *Revolver*

15. d — *Rubber Soul*

16. a — *Yellow Submarine*

17. b — Phil Spector

18. False

19. c — *Help!*

DID YOU KNOW?

- *Please Please Me* was The Beatles' debut album in the UK and was mostly recorded in one 13-hour-long recording session. Ten out of the 14 tracks were recorded in that session. It was produced by EMI's Parlophone label under George Martin and released on March 22, 1963.

- On November 22, 1963, exactly eight months after The Beatles' debut album release, *With the Beatles* premiered and replaced its predecessor at the top of the British chart. Some of the songs on it were featured in *Introducing... The Beatles*, the first LP the band released in the United States.

- Parlophone was an imprint of EMI (Electrical and Musical Industries), a multi-industry company founded in London. EMI's American label at the time was Capitol Records. Initially, Capitol Records was reluctant to release Beatles records in the US, and Vee-Jay Records of Chicago beat them to the punch with the release of *Introducing... The Beatles!* on January 10, 1964. Ten days later, Capitol Records released the album *Meet the Beatles*.

- Prior to *A Hard Day's Night*, The Beatles albums had been a combination of original songs and covers. Released on July 10, 1964, *A Hard Day's Night* is the first Beatles album to feature all original songs and music, and the only one to be written entirely by Lennon and McCartney.

- Beatlemania was at its peak in 1964, which demanded a hectic performing and touring schedule for the band. Released on December 4, 1964, *Beatles for Sale* contains eight tracks of original compositions, and the remaining six are covers. The original songs introduced moodier, sophisticated lyricism along with ventures into studio experimentation.

- *Help!* is the fifth studio album of The Beatles, and was also the soundtrack to a movie of the same name. It was first released in the UK on August 6, 1965 under Parlophone, and then seven days later in the US under Capitol.

- Released on December 3, 1965, *Rubber Soul* was the first album the band was able to record without any film, radio, or concert commitments at the same time. The title is a pun referring to the soles of shoes and was inspired by a critic who judged that the Rolling Stones were "good, but plastic soul."

- On August 5, 1966, The Beatles released *Revolver*. Later that month they would play their final concert before retiring from touring. This album is recognized for its overt use of studio technology, musical styles, and psychedelic content.

- The legendary *Sgt. Pepper's Lonely Hearts Club Band* is regarded as an early concept album that brought recognition to albums as an art form. The album's cover features 58 iconic individuals, such as Albert Einstein, Shirley Temple, Marilyn Monroe, Bob Dylan, and Edgar Allan Poe.

- *Magical Mystery Tour* is an additional soundtrack album to a television film of the same name. It continued the band's exploration of psychedelic sounds and studio experimentation.

- The self-titled album *The Beatles* is more often referred to as the *White Album.* Released on November 22, 1968 under Apple Records, its plain white sleeve directly and intentionally contrasted with their earlier, exuberant album artwork. Most of the songs on this album were written while The Beatles were studying meditation in India.

- To The Beatles, *Yellow Submarine* was largely filling a contractual obligation to supply new songs for the animated film. Released in the US first on January 13, 1969, this album contains six tracks from The Beatles, four of them new. The remaining tracks are recordings of the score of the film, which was written by George Martin.

- Named after the location of what was at the time EMI Studios, the cover of *Abbey Road* features the famous image of The Beatles walking across Abbey Road in London. It was released on September 26, 1969 by Apple Records, but it was recorded after sessions for their final album release, *Let It Be.*

- *Let It Be*, the final studio album releases by The Beatles, was released on May 8, 1970 after the group's breakup. It was originally titled *Get Back* and was reassembled by American producer Phil Spector after the project had been abandoned.

CHAPTER 5:

SONGS

TRIVIA TIME!

1. As the first song to be released on their own Apple Records, which Beatles title was written by Paul McCartney for and about John Lennon's son, Julian Lennon?

    a. "Don't Worry, Jules"
    b. "Come Together"
    c. "Julia"
    d. "Hey Jude"

2. Which Beatles song served as an anthem for the flower power movement embraced by the counterculture of the 1960s?

    a. "All You Need Is Love"
    b. "Little Child"
    c. "With a Little Help from My Friends"
    d. "Across the Universe"

3. Which Beatles song has been covered over two thousand times, making it their most covered song?

a. "Let It Be"
b. "Yesterday"
c. "Hey Jude"
d. "She Loves You"

4. Before their first visit to the US, which single released in the US would become their first American number one hit?

a. "I Want to Hold Your Hand"
b. "With a Little Help from My Friends"
c. "She Loves You"
d. "All You Need Is Love"

5. Featuring two orchestral glissandos, which Beatles song ends on a sustained chord played on several keyboards that lasts for roughly forty seconds?

a. "Sgt. Pepper's Lonely Hearts Club Band"
b. "Strawberry Fields Forever"
c. "A Day in the Life"
d. "Something"

6. Written by George Harrison, which Beatles song was the single for the album *Abbey Road* and Frank Sinatra's favorite by the band?

a. "Here Comes the Sun"
b. "Golden Slumbers"
c. "Get Back"
d. "Something"

7. True or False: "Strawberry Fields Forever" is not based on a real place.

8. The title of which Beatles song shares its name with a suburban street in Liverpool?

    a. "Blue Jay Way"
    b. "Penny Lane"
    c. "Helter Skelter"
    d. "Nowhere Man"

9. True or False: "Come Together" was originally intended as a campaign song.

10. Which Beatles song was inspired by Julian Lennon's childhood drawing of his classmate?

    a. "Julia"
    b. "Long Tall Sally"
    c. "Lucy in the Sky with Diamonds"
    d. "I Am the Walrus"

11. Released in 1963, which Beatles single remains the band's best-selling single in the UK?

    a. "I Saw Her Standing There"
    b. "Octopus's Garden"
    c. "Drive My Car"
    d. "She Loves You"

12. What was the first explicitly political song The Beatles released?

    a. "Revolution"
    b. "The Fool on the Hill"
    c. "Her Majesty"
    d. "Please Mr. Postman"

13. Which gospel-tinged Beatles hit was inspired by a dream and starts with Paul's singing and piano?

    a. "Let It Be"
    b. "Yesterday"
    c. "For No One"
    d. "I Saw Her Standing There"

14. True or False: "Yesterday" started with the words "scrambled eggs" before the lyrics were finalized.

15. Ringo Starr wrote two songs by himself for The Beatles: "Don't Pass Me By" and which other song?

    a. "Every Little Thing"
    b. "Yellow Submarine"
    c. "Octopus's Garden"
    d. "A Hard Day's Night"

16. Which Beatles song was partially inspired by racial tensions in the United States?

    a. "I'm So Tired"
    b. "Blackbird"
    c. "The Long and Winding Road"
    d. "Rain"

17. How many Beatles recordings feature vocals from Ringo Starr?

    a. 5
    b. 13
    c. 26
    d. 11

18. True or False: Eleanor Rigby was a real person but Paul McCartney denies writing the song about her.

ANSWERS

1. d—"Hey Jude"

2. a—"All You Need Is Love"

3. b—"Yesterday"

4. a—"I Want to Hold Your Hand"

5. c—"A Day in the Life"

6. d—"Something"

7. False

8. b—"Penny Lane"

9. True

10. c—"Lucy in the Sky with Diamonds"

11. d—"She Loves You"

12. a—"Revolution"

13. a—"Let It Be"

14. True

15. c—"Octopus's Garden"

16. b—"Blackbird"

17. d—11

18. True

DID YOU KNOW?

- The songwriting partnership of John Lennon and Paul McCartney is probably the most successful musical collaboration ever. While they did co-write many songs, most of the jointly credited songs were either written by Lennon or McCartney, but because they had made an agreement, the songs were also credited to the partnership.

- The release of "I Want to Hold Your Hand" launched the so-called British Invasion into the American music scene and ignited Beatlemania in the US.

- Strawberry Field was an orphanage in Liverpool close to where John Lennon grew up. The location is currently a historical exhibit with the same name. There is also a memorial garden named "Strawberry Fields" in Central Park in honor of Lennon.

- The historic ending chord of "A Day in the Life" inspired the creation of the sound known as the "Deep Note" trademarked by the George Lucas formed company THX.

- Despite the suggestive initial of the noun titles, John Lennon and Paul McCartney have denied the rumors of "Lucy in the Sky with Diamonds" being a song about LSD. Lennon attributes the song to Julian's drawing of his classmate, Lucy O'Donnell, along with imagery from Lewis Carroll's *Alice in Wonderland* books.

- The sitar in "Norwegian Wood (This Bird Has Flown)" is the first appearance of the Indian string instrument in a rock recording from Western music. The track is considered developmental to the raga rock and psychedelic rock of the mid-1960s and is also a key work in the early evolution of world music.

CHAPTER 6:

TELEVISION AND MOVIES

TRIVIA TIME!

1. Which 1964 movie constituted The Beatles' film debut?

   a. *Help!*
   b. *A Hard Day's Night*
   c. *Magical Mystery Tour*
   d. *Yellow Submarine*

2. Granada Studio in Manchester was the first to host The Beatles in their first televised live performance on which program in 1962?

   a. World in Action
   b. People and Places
   c. Connections
   d. Stars in Their Eyes

3. The Beatles' first live television performance in the US was on which show?

   a. The Lucy Show
   b. The Danny Thomas Show
   c. The Dick Van Dyke Show

d. The Ed Sullivan Show

4. How much money did SNL's Lorne Michaels offer the Beatles if all four of them made an appearance together on the show?

   a. $1,000
   b. $2,000
   c. $3,000
   d. $4,000

5. True or False: All of The Beatles' films released in the 1960s have a coinciding album soundtrack of the same name.

6. The Beatles starred in how many major motion pictures as a band?

   a. 1
   b. 3
   c. 4
   d. 10

7. An animated musical fantasy, which film featured cartoon versions of The Beatles?

   a. *Yellow Submarine*
   b. *Magical Mystery Tour*
   c. *Across the Universe*
   d. *Help!*

8. Which famous musician was a teen extra in the film *A Hard Day's Night,* but did not actually appear in the movie?

   a. Jimi Hendrix
   b. Phil Collins
   c. Elvis Presley

d. David Bowie

9. Which Beatles film is a documentary of their making of an album, observing the band from a "fly on the wall" perspective?

   a. *Magical Mystery Tour*
   b. *Around the Beatles*
   c. *Let It Be*
   d. *I Met the Walrus*

10. While all four Beatles were involved in films individually, which Beatle received the most praise and acted in several movies in addition to The Beatles' films?

    a. Paul McCartney
    b. John Lennon
    c. George Harrison
    d. Ringo Starr

11. Broadcasted in 1963, which BBC show was The Beatles' first national television appearance in the UK?

    a. *Doctor Who*
    b. *The 625 Show*
    c. *The Sky at Night*
    d. *BBC News*

12. True or False: The Beatles are often credited with inventing the music video.

13. Which major film featuring The Beatles was the group's first film shot in color?

    a. *Help!*
    b. *A Hard Day's Night*
    c. *Magical Mystery Tour*

d. *Yellow Submarine*

14. True or False: The Beatles never had an animated television series.

15. Which character did John Lennon play in Richard Lester's satirical film *How I Won the War*?
    a. Sanders
    b. Gripweed
    c. Kermit
    d. Garp

16. Being fans of the book series, which prolific trilogy were The Beatles interested in adapting into a film, but weren't able to put together due to lack of a director and rights to the story?
    a. The Lord of the Rings
    b. Sherlock Holmes
    c. My Family and Other Animals
    d. Gormenghast

17. Which hour-long television special that featured several groups had The Beatles take part in two segments (a musical set and spoof of a scene from Shakespeare's *A Midsummer Night's Dream*)?
    a. *It's The Beatles*
    b. *Juke Box Jury*
    c. *Around The Beatles*
    d. *Literary Music*

18. What was the title of the first live international satellite television broadcast, which featured The Beatles' debut performance of "All You Need is Love"?
    a. *Our Bands*

b. *Our People*

c. *Our Music*

d. *Our World*

19. Released in 1979, which Beatles biographical film has the distinction of being the only one about The Beatles to be made while John Lennon was still alive?

a. *Backbeat*

b. *I Wanna Hold Your Hand*

c. *Birth of The Beatles*

d. *Good Ol' Freda*

ANSWERS

1. b — *A Hard Day's Night*

2. b — People and Places

3. d — The Ed Sullivan Show

4. c — $3,000

5. True

6. c — 5

7. a — *Yellow Submarine*

8. b — Phil Collins

9. c — *Let It Be*

10. d — Ringo Starr

11. b — *The 625 Show*

12. True

13. a — *Help!*

14. False

15. b — Gripweed

16. a — The Lord of the Rings

17. c — *Around The Beatles*

18. d — *Our World*

19. c — *Birth of The Beatles*

DID YOU KNOW?

- *A Hard Day's Night* was a musical comedy film and The Beatles' movie debut. The mockumentary portrays 36 hours of the group preparing for a London television performance. It was directed by Robert Lester and remains an influential jukebox musical.

- *Magical Mystery Tour* was a television film rather than a feature film and ran for under an hour. The plot follows a group of people on a mystery tour in 1967 aboard a coach bus. Throughout the tour, strange things occur at the whim of a few magicians.

- Inspired by the music of The Beatles, *Yellow Submarine* is an animated musical adventure film featuring cartoon versions of The Beatles. The group had little input in this film but did appear at the end for a live-action scene. They did not voice their animated characters.

- A number of documentaries have been created for The Beatles as well as several films and television programs portraying the members of the group. There are also several fictional films that are entirely based on Beatles themes and songs, most recently the 2019 film *Yesterday*.

CHAPTER 7:

FAMOUS MOMENTS

TRIVIA TIME!

1. True or False: In their 1965 tour, The Beatles were the first band to perform a major stadium concert.

2. How many people watched The Beatles' debut on the American television program, *The Ed Sullivan Show?*

    a. About 10 million
    b. About 20 million
    c. About 50 million
    d. About 75 million

3. True or False: When The Beatles auditioned for George Martin, he was immediately impressed by their music.

4. In which hotel was the meeting between Bob Dylan and The Beatles?

    a. Hilton Hotel
    b. Delmonico Hotel
    c. The Plaza Hotel
    d. MGM Grand

5. On August 15, 1965, The Beatles played one of their biggest shows up to that point (in terms of crowd size) at which stadium?

   a. Shea Stadium
   b. Anaheim Stadium
   c. Fenway Park
   d. Madison Square Garden

6. In which year did the group's bassist, Stuart Sutcliffe, first get the haircut that was quickly adopted by the rest of the band?

   a. 1959
   b. 1960
   c. 1961
   d. 1962

7. True or False: The Beatles traveled to India to study and meditate with Maharishi, but all of them left early.

8. Which country did The Beatles flee after upsetting political leaders by declining an offer for a breakfast reception?

   a. Indonesia
   b. Japan
   c. Sri Lanka
   d. The Philippines

9. True or False: The Beatles famously performed at the Woodstock Festival in 1969.

10. Which Beatle quit the band for two weeks due to inter-group tensions while recording *The White Album*?

   a. John Lennon
   b. Paul McCartney

c. George Harrison

d. Ringo Starr

11. Following *The White Album*, The Beatles staged their final live performance on the rooftop of which company's headquarters?

   a. Apple Corps

   b. Warner Music

   c. Sony Music

   d. BMG

12. True or False: In 1964, the Beatles famously held the top five slots of the Billboard Hot 100 Chart at the same time.

13. Approximately how many people greeted The Beatles when they landed at JFK airport, arriving in the US for the first time?

   a. 2,000

   b. 3,000

   c. 4,000

   d. 5,000

14. Near which beach was the gym where The Beatles met Muhammad Ali?

   a. Coronado Beach

   b. Clearwater Beach

   c. Santa Monica Beach

   d. Miami Beach

15. At which hotel chain did John Lennon and Yoko Ono hold the part of their "bed-in-for-peace" held in Amsterdam?

   a. Renaissance

   b. DoubleTree

   c. Hilton

d. Volkshotel

16. Which Beatle is barefoot on the album cover of *Abbey Road*?

   a. John Lennon
   b. Paul McCartney
   c. George Harrison
   d. Ringo Starr

17. True or False: The BBC banned the song "I Am the Walrus" due to its suggestive lyrics.

18. How long was John Lennon's infamous "lost weekend"?

   a. 2 days
   b. 4 days
   c. 11 months
   d. 18 months

ANSWERS

1. True

2. d — About 75 million people

3. False

4. b — Delmonico Hotel

5. a — Shea Stadium

6. b — 1960

7. True

8. d — The Philippines

9. False

10. d — Ringo Starr

11. a — Apple Corps

12. True

13. c — 4,000

14. d — Miami Beach

15. c — Hilton

16. b — Paul McCartney

17. True

18. d — 18 months

DID YOU KNOW?

- The Beatles' unannounced rooftop concert that ended up being the group's final performance lasted for about forty-two minutes atop the Apple Corps headquarters before the Metropolitan Police arrived and asked that the band reduce the volume, shutting down the party.

- In 1967, The Beatles wanted to purchase a set of Greek islands where they were planning to live together alongside family and friends. After visiting the island and surrounding areas, they intended to buy it but lost interest when there was a delay due to currency exchange.

- It is reported that George Martin was mostly underwhelmed by The Beatles' music at their first recording and audition at Abbey Road Studios, which at the time was EMI Studios. Their witty charm and quips are said to have ultimately won him over. When Martin asked if they had any complaints, George Harrison responded, "Well, for a start, I don't like your tie."

- In 1973, a few years after The Beatles had split, John Lennon was having marital troubles with Yoko Ono and left with his assistant and girlfriend, May Pang. His drunken antics made headlines, and he also wrote a lot of music during this "lost weekend" that lasted around 18 months.

CHAPTER 8:

CONTROVERSY

TRIVIA TIME!

1. Known as the "butcher cover," which album's original cover shows The Beatles dressed in white coats covered with raw meat and dismembered baby dolls?

   a. *Beatles for Sale*
   b. *Revolver*
   c. *Yesterday and Today*
   d. *Please Please Me*

2. Which member of The Beatles made the comment that the group had become "more popular than Jesus"?

   a. John Lennon
   b. Ringo Starr
   c. Paul McCartney
   d. George Harrison

3. True or False: The BBC banned the song "Lucy in the Sky with Diamonds."

4. Which member of The Beatles was the subject of a conspiracy theory to have died and been replaced by an

imposter?

a. John Lennon
b. Ringo Starr
c. Paul McCartney
d. George Harrison

5. True or False: The Beatles were against drugs.

6. Which Beatles song is sadly linked to the cult lunatics of Charles Manson?

a. "Helter Skelter"
b. "I Am the Walrus"
c. "Get Back"
d. "Maxwell's Silver Hammer"

7. True or False: The Beatles' first imprint done in America spelled the band's name incorrectly, adding an extra "t."

8. The Beatles' music initially got very little traction in America until which song was released, turning public opinion around?

a. "Please Please Me"
b. "I Wanna Hold Your Hand"
c. "From Me to You"
d. "She Loves You"

9. When the USSR banned The Beatles and their records from the country, which type of underground media did young Soviets use to obtain Beatles music instead of paying high prices for real black market vinyls?

a. Cassette tapes
b. X-ray films
c. Compact discs

d. Digital downloads

10. What is the name of the British police officer who headed the Drug Squad, arresting The Beatles and many other celebrities on drug charges during the 1960s?

   a. Derek Faber
   b. Norman Pilcher
   c. Chad Lomner
   d. Paul Brimmer

11. Which American actress initially declined to have her likeness put on the cover of *Sgt. Pepper's Lonely Hearts Club Band* before receiving a letter personally mailed by The Beatles?

   a. Shirley Temple
   b. Mae West
   c. Marilyn Monroe
   d. Bette Davis

12. Why were Paul McCartney and Pete Best arrested in Hamburg and deported from Germany in 1960?

   a. Possession of drugs
   b. Suspicion of arson
   c. Receiving public assistance
   d. Underage

13. While the other three were on holiday in Santa Cruz, which Beatle went on holiday with their manager Brian Epstein in Barcelona at the same time?

   a. Paul McCartney
   b. John Lennon
   c. Ringo Starr

d. George Harrison

14. True or False: Paul McCartney had an affair with Ringo Starr's wife, Maureen.

15. How many days before the release of the album *Abbey Road* did John Lennon secretly announce his plans to leave the band?

    a. 1
    b. 6
    c. 13
    d. 17

16. What was the final listed song on The Beatles' last recorded album, a title that fittingly described where the band was heading?

    a. "Let It Be"
    b. "The End"
    c. "It's Over"
    d. "The Long and Winding Road"

17. While isolating himself with his family in Scotland, which Beatle took part in a Q&A with select journalists who would interpret his remarks as the breakup of the band?

    a. John Lennon
    b. Paul McCartney
    c. Ringo Starr
    d. George Harrison

18. On what date did Mark David Chapman shoot and kill John Lennon?

    a. September 15, 1980
    b. October 12, 1980
    c. November 10, 1980

d. December 8, 1980

ANSWERS

1. c — *Yesterday and Today*

2. a — John Lennon

3. True

4. c — Paul McCartney

5. False

6. a — "Helter Skelter"

7. True

8. b — "I Wanna Hold Your Hand"

9. b — X-ray films

10. b — Norman Pilcher

11. b — Mae West

12. b — Suspicion of arson

13. b — John Lennon

14. False

15. b — 6

16. a — Paul McCartney

17. b — "The End"

18. b — Paul McCartney

19. d — December 8, 1980

DID YOU KNOW?

- Rumors of a scandalous affair surrounded Brian Epstein and John Lennon's holiday in Barcelona. Upon their return, news was circulating of a potential love affair, although John's wife Cynthia had just given birth to their first son, Julian.

- For decades, rumors have circulated that the person, Sgt. Pepper, from the album cover is actually Aleister Crowley, the "wickedest man in the world."

- The Beatles might be the original starters of the "devil horns" hand sign. If you look closely at John's hand on the cover of *Yellow Submarine,* you will see that it isn't the "I love you" hand sign that many try to argue is there. However, he is doing the sign in reverse.

- Quincy Jones called The Beatles "the worst musicians in the world" along with a few profane statements implying that they couldn't play, singling out McCartney as "the worst bass player I ever heard." The pair later made amends, and it is now water under the bridge.

- As tensions in the band grew, George's marriage to Pattie Boyd began to disintegrate, and he started having an affair with Ringo's wife in the early '70s. After leaving George, Boyd would go on to marry Eric Clapton, who had been in love with her and wrote "Layla" about his feelings for her in 1971.

- Although John privately announced his departure first, it was kept secret for business reasons. It was the Q & A press release remarks from Paul McCartney that were interpreted as an announcement of the band breaking up, making headlines around the world.

CHAPTER 9:

COLLABORATIONS

TRIVIA TIME!

1. Which Beatles song, written by George Harrison, featured lead guitar by Eric Clapton?

    a. "Something"
    b. "Here Comes the Sun"
    c. "While My Guitar Gently Weeps"
    d. "I'm Only Sleeping"

2. In the recording of the song "Let It Be," who is playing the organ?

    a. Alan Price
    b. Rod Argent
    c. James Brown
    d. Billy Preston

3. Who was recruited by George Harrison to join sessions for "Get Back" in an attempt to quell rising tensions in the band?

    a. Eric Clapton

b. Billy Preston

c. Mick Jagger

d. Elton John

4. What was the name of the session drummer who recorded The Beatles' first single release, "Love Me Do," in 1962?

a. Jeremy Bold

b. Andy White

c. Keith Richard

d. Buddy Rich

5. Which track from the *Help!* soundtrack featured a flute part at the end added by Johnnie Scott?

a. "Dizzy Miss Lizzie"

b. "Ticket to Ride"

c. "The Night Before"

d. "You've Got to Hide Your Love Away"

6. Featuring George Martin on keys, which Beatles song contains a baroque piano solo midway?

a. "In My Life"

b. "Eleanor Rigby"

c. "A Day in the Life"

d. "Yesterday"

7. The song "For No One" from *Revolver* got a big boost from which brass instrument played by Alan Civil?

a. Trumpet

b. Trombone

c. French horn

d. Tuba

8. While watching a television performance by a high-pitched trumpet, which Beatles song did Paul McCartney

decide to embellish with a piccolo trumpet played by David Mason?

a. "Hey Jude"
b. "The Fool on the Hill"
c. "Penny Lane"
d. "Let It Be"

9. Which Harrison composition for The Beatles enlisted the help of four musicians from the Asian Music Circle to add to the melding of Eastern and Western music?

a. "Within You Without You"
b. "Here Comes the Sun"
c. "Norwegian Wood (This Bird Has Flown)"
d. "I Me Mine"

10. While George Martin took vacation, Chris Thomas stepped in as temporary band producer and played the harpsichord on which Beatles song written by George Harrison?

a. "Old Brown Shoe"
b. "Lady Madonna"
c. "Roll Over Beethoven"
d. "Piggies"

11. Before his death in 1969, which band leader and founder recorded a saxophone solo on The Beatles song "You Know My Name (Look Up My Number)"?

a. Mick Jagger
b. Brian Jones
c. Bob Dylan
d. Dave Davies

12. True or False: After The Beatles disbanded and started

their solo careers, they never had any post-breakup collaborations with each other.

13. How many anthology albums have been recorded for *The Beatles Anthology* series?

    a. 1
    b. 2
    c. 3
    d. 4

14. Originally written and recorded in 1977 as a home demo, which John Lennon composition was released 15 years after Lennon's murder, incorporating contributions from the other three Beatles?

    a. "Woman"
    b. "Cold Turkey"
    c. "Now and Then"
    d. "Free as a Bird"

15. The Beatles song "She's Leaving Home" featured a harp played by which female musician (the first woman to appear on a Beatles record)?

    a. Sheila Bromberg
    b. Yoko Ono
    c. Janis Joplin
    d. Brenda Missando

16. A 16-piece choir of professional studio vocalists was included as backup vocals on which Beatles song?

    a. "All You Need is Love"
    b. "I Want to Hold Your Hand"
    c. "I Am the Walrus"

d. "Yellow Submarine"

17. Found on *The White Album*, "The Continuing Story of Bungalow Bill" was recorded with lead vocals by a non-member. Who was it?

    a. Yoko Ono
    b. Janis Joplin
    c. Elton John
    d. Billy Preston

18. Which Rolling Stones single was penned by The Beatles and recorded by both bands?

    a. "Satisfaction"
    b. "Time Is on My Side"
    c. "I Wanna Be Your Man"
    d. "Paint It Black"

19. True or False: All of The Beatles' guests during their *Our World* recording and videotaping sang on the song "All You Need is Love" during its lengthy fade-out ending.

ANSWERS

1. c — "While My Guitar Gently Weeps"

2. d — Billy Preston

3. b — Billy Preston

4. b — Andy White

5. d — "You've Got to Hide Your Love Away"

6. a — "In My Life"

7. c — French horn

8. c — "Penny Lane"

9. a — "Within You Without You"

10. d — "Piggies"

11. b — Brian Jones

12. False

13. c — 3

14. d — "Free as a Bird"

15. a — Sheila Bromberg

16. c — "I Am the Walrus"

17. a — Yoko Ono

18. c — "I Wanna Be Your Man"

19. True

DID YOU KNOW?

- After replacing Pete Best with Ringo Starr, George Martin was still not convinced of Ringo's abilities and brought in session drummer Andy White to record the single "Love Me Do." Ringo went on to record the album version.

- The baroque piano solo in the middle of "In My Life" was a little too involved for any of The Beatles to play. George Martin couldn't quite handle it either, but he had the brilliant idea to record the solo at half-speed and then speed up the tape to fit the song.

- For the *Our World* filming, it was decided that The Beatles, other than Ringo Starr, would perform on high stools in the studio, surrounded by friends sitting cross-legged on the floor. Friends and family in attendance included Mick Jagger, Marianne Faithfull, Keith Richard, Keith Moon, Eric Clapton, Pattie Boyd, Jane Asher, Mike McCartney, Graham Nash, and Hunter Davies.

CHAPTER 10:

AWARDS AND HONORS

TRIVIA TIME!

1. Which of the principal members was the first to be inducted into the Hall of Fame as an individual?

   a. John Lennon
   b. Paul McCartney
   c. Ringo Starr
   d. George Harrison

2. True or False: Paul McCartney and Ringo Starr have been knighted by the Queen of England.

3. On their behalf, who accepted The Beatles' Oscar for "Best Original Song Score" at the 43rd Academy Awards in 1970?

   a. Yoko Ono
   b. Eric Clapton
   c. Quincy Jones
   d. Phil Spector

4. In 1969, 4 years after receiving the MBE (Members of the

Most Excellent Order of the British Empire) Award, which Beatle returned the award in protest of British involvement in the war in Biafra and support for the US in the Vietnam War?

a. Ringo Starr
b. John Lennon
c. George Harrison
d. Paul McCartney

5. Earning one of their first Grammys at the 8th Annual Grammy Awards in 1965, The Beatles won "Best Performance by a Vocal Group" for which film?

a. *Help!*
b. *Magical Mystery Tour*
c. *Let It Be*
d. *A Hard Day's Night*

6. True or False: The Beatles won a Grammy for "Best New Artist" in 1960.

7. At the 10th Annual Grammy Awards, The Beatles received two awards and two nominations for which album?

a. *Abbey Road*
b. *Sgt. Pepper's Lonely Hearts Club Band*
c. *Revolver*
d. *Let It Be*

8. Which special merit award did The Beatles win in 1972 for having made significant contributions to the field of recording?

a. Grammy Trustees Award
b. Lifetime Achievement Award
c. Grammy Legend Award
d. Merit Grammy

9. True or False: The Beatles continued to win awards long after the band split.

10. In which year were The Beatles inducted into the Hall of Fame as a group?

    a. 1985
    b. 1987
    c. 1988
    d. 1999

11. Which Beatles album was the first to be inducted into the Grammy Hall of Fame, an institution that honors historical recordings?

    a. *Abbey Road*
    b. *Revolver*
    c. *Sgt. Pepper's Lonely Hearts Club Band*
    d. *Rubber Soul*

12. Which song written by McCartney and Lennon won the Grammy for Song of the Year in 1966?

    a. "I Am the Walrus"
    b. "Michelle"
    c. "A Day in the Life"
    d. "Come Together"

13. In which year did The Beatles win three Grammys?

    a. 1965
    b. 1977
    c. 1985
    d. 1997

14. At the 56th Annual Grammy Awards in 2014, The Beatles won a prestigious Grammy for which award?

a. Grammy Legend Award
b. Grammy Trustees Award
c. Grammy Hall of Fame Award
d. Lifetime Achievement Award

15. On which day is Global Beatles Day/World Beatles Day celebrated annually?

    a. June 25th
    b. July 25th
    c. August 25th
    d. September 25th

16. True or False: Each member of The Beatles has an asteroid named after them.

17. Altogether, how many The Beatles singles and albums have been inducted into the Grammy Hall of Fame?

    a. 12
    b. 15
    c. 16
    d. 18

18. Which magazine included The Beatles on their list of "20th century's 100 most influential people"?

    a. People
    b. Rolling Stone
    c. Time
    d. Entertainment Weekly

19. How many Grammys have The Beatles been awarded?

    a. 5
    b. 7
    c. 10

d. 18

20. Which top-selling Beatles album was surprisingly not even nominated for a Grammy despite its popularity at the time?

a. *The White Album*
b. *Abbey Road*
c. *Help!*
d. *Yellow Submarine*

ANSWERS

1. a — John Lennon

2. True

3. c — Quincy Jones

4. b — John Lennon

5. d — *A Hard Day's Night*

6. False

7. b — *Sgt Pepper's Lonely Hearts Club Band*

8. a — The Grammy Trustees Award

9. True

10. c — 1988

11. c — *Sgt. Pepper's Lonely Hearts Club Band*

12. b — "Michelle"

13. d — 1997

14. d — The Lifetime Achievement Award

15. a — June 25th

16. True

17. b — 15

18. c — Time

19. b — 7

20. a — *The White Album*

DID YOU KNOW?

- In 1964, The Beatles won three Ivor Novello Awards, two of them being "The Most Broadcast Work of the Year" and "The 'A' Side of the Record Which Achieved the Highest Certified British Sales" for the song "She Loves You." The third Ivor Novello Award that year was the "Special Award for Outstanding Services to British Music."

- 1965 brought The Beatles their next Ivor Novello Awards for "Most Performed Work of the Year" and "The 'A' Side of the Record Which Achieved the Highest Certified British Sales" with the song "Can't Buy Me Love." They also received their first Grammy that year for the previous year's *A Hard Day's Night,* earning them "Best Performance by a Vocal Group" in addition to "Best New Artist of 1964."

- The Beatles won two Ivor Novello Awards in 1966 for "The 'A' Side with Highest Certified British Sales" with the song "We Can Work It Out" and "Outstanding Song" for "Yesterday."

- The "Grammy for Song of the Year" in 1966 was awarded to McCartney and Lennon for the song "Michelle." McCartney also won the award for "Best Contemporary (R&R) Solo Vocal Performance, Male or Female" for his singing on "Eleanor Rigby." The group won two more Ivor Novello Awards this year as well — one for the song "Michelle" as "The Most Performed Work of the Year" and the second for "Yellow Submarine" as "The 'A' Side with the Highest Certified British Sales."

- *Sgt. Pepper's Lonely Hearts Club Band* won The Beatles two Grammys in 1968—"Album of the Year" and "Best Contemporary Album." In the same year, they also received their tenth Ivor Novello Award for "Best British Song, Musically and Lyrically" for the song "She's Leaving Home."

- The Awit Awards are music awards given in the Philippines to recognize outstanding achievements in the music industry. In 1969, The Beatles won an Awit Award for "Vocal Group of the Year—Foreign." They also won an Ivor Novello Award for "Hey Jude" being "The 'A' Side with the Highest Certified British Sales."

- 1970 brought two more Ivor Novello Awards—"The 'A' Side with the Highest Certified British Sales" for "Get Back" and "The Most Performed Work of the Year" for "Ob-La-Di Ob-La-Da."

- The Beatles landed the Grammy for "Best Original Score Written for Motion Picture" for *Let It Be*" in 1971 along with their 15th and final Ivor Novello Award for "Something" as "The Best Song Musically and Lyrically."

- In 1977, The Beatles won three Brit Awards—"British Album of the Year" with *Sgt. Pepper's Lonely Hearts Club Band*, the award for "Best British Group," and the award for "Outstanding Contribution to Music." In 1983, they won an additional Brit Award for "Outstanding Contribution to Music."

- In 1984, the MTV VMAs awarded The Beatles the "Video Vanguard Award" in the ceremony's inaugural year for essentially inventing the music video.

- The Beatles were inducted into The Rock and Roll Hall of Fame as a group in 1988. The individual members of the band would be inducted at later dates.

- There were three Grammy wins for The Beatles in 1997 — "Best Music Video, Long Form" for *The Beatles Anthology,* "Best Music Video, Short Form" for "Free as a Bird," and "Best Pop Performance by a Duo or Group with Vocal" for "Free as a Bird."

- Founded in 1989, the World Music Awards is an international award ceremony that honors the best-selling most popular artist. In 2001, The Beatles won the award for "World's Best Selling Pop Rock Artists/Group" and "World's Best Selling British Artists." In 2008, they won the "Chopard Diamond Award" presented by the WMA, which celebrates recording artists who have sold over 100 million albums throughout their career.

- The UK Hall of Fame started in 2004, and The Beatles were inducted that first year. In this same year, *Rolling Stone* magazine ranked The Beatles as the most significant and influential rock music artist of the last 50 years.

- Many of The Beatles' later compilation and reissue albums have received awards. In 1996, *Anthology 1* won the "Q Award for Best Reissue/Compilation." The album *1* was awarded the Billboard Music Award for "Album of the Year" and Meteor Music Award for "Best Selling International Group Album" in 2001. In 2010, *The Beatles Remastered* landed a MOJO Award for "Catalogue Release of the Year."

- The Beatles' final Grammy to date is the "Lifetime Achievement Award," which they won in 2014.

- Published in 1999, *Time* magazine recognized The Beatles on their list of the "20th century's 100 most important people."

- The NME (New Musical Express) Awards have chosen The Beatles for 17 awards, including "World Vocal Group"; "British Vocal Group"; "Best British Disc"; "Best British LP"; "Outstanding Vocal Group"; "Top British Group"; and "Best Band Ever."

CHAPTER 11:

STATS AND RECORDS

TRIVIA TIME!

1. In which year did The Beatles have songs occupying Numbers 1-5 on the Billboard Hot 100, being the first and only band to do so?

   a. 1962
   b. 1964
   c. 1966
   d. 1968

2. During their time as a band from 1962-1969, how many number one hits did The Beatles place on the Billboard charts?

   a. 10
   b. 20
   c. 50
   d. 100

3. True or False: The Beatles are the second best-selling artist of all time.

4. In 2019, which Beatles album extended their record for longest time for an album to return to number one, doing so after nearly 50 years?

   a. *Abbey Road*
   b. *Let It Be*
   c. *Sgt. Pepper's Lonely Hearts Club Band*
   d. *The Beatles/The White Album*

5. Approximately how many albums have The Beatles sold worldwide?

   a. 10 million
   b. 500 million
   c. 600 million
   d. 1 billion

6. How many Beatles albums have made it to the top of the Billboard album charts?

   a. 4
   b. 9
   c. 14
   d. 19

7. True or False: The Beatles have six albums that have achieved RIAA Certified Diamond status in the United States.

8. In the UK, The Beatles were the first band to be featured on what item in 2007?

   a. Postage stamps
   b. Postcards
   c. Billboards

d. Folders

9. In 1981, how many The Beatles albums were on the US Top 200, the first time for that to happen simultaneously within a year?

   a. 2
   b. 3
   c. 4
   d. 7

10. Purchased at an auction by Jim Pattison in 1985, current owner of Guinness World Records, which item previously owned by John Lennon holds the record for most expensive The Beatles memorabilia?

    a. Steinway & Sons Model Z upright piano
    b. Rickenbacker 325 guitar
    c. 1965 Phantom V Rolls-Royce
    d. His round glasses

11. How many songs did The Beatles release between 1962-1970?

    a. 153
    b. 183
    c. 213
    d. 353

12. In their time as a band, how many top ten Billboard hits did The Beatles produce?

    a. 30
    b. 32
    c. 34
    d. 36

13. True or False: Although the songs were credited to the Lennon-McCartney partnership, Lennon actually wrote 61 songs to McCartney's 43 for The Beatles.

14. The Beatles' longest running number one hit song "Hey Jude" kept its number one spot for how many weeks?

    a. 9 weeks

    b. 15 weeks

    c. 19 weeks

    d. 21 weeks

15. True or False: *Anthology 1, Anthology 2,* and *Anthology 3* all claimed the number one spots within two years in the 1990s.

16. In the UK, how many weeks did The Beatles hold the number one spot with single releases?

    a. 69

    b. 60

    c. 55

    d. 50

17. How many albums are in the "core" catalogue for The Beatles?

    a. 12

    b. 14

    c. 16

    d. 18

18. What number are The Beatles ranked in *Billboard* magazine's all-time most successful Hot 100 artists?

    a. number one

b. No. 2

c. No. 3

d. No. 4

19. True or False: The Beatles' albums were released the same in all countries that distributed their music.

ANSWERS

20. b — 1964

21. b — 20

22. False

23. a — Abbey Road

24. c — 600 million

25. d — 19

26. True

27. a — Postage stamps

28. d — 7

29. c — 1965 Phantom V Rolls-Royce

30. c — 213

31. c — 34

32. True

33. a — 9 weeks

34. True

35. a — 69

36. a — 12

37. a — number one

38. False

DID YOU KNOW?

- The Beatles hold records in the UK for most number one albums on UK albums charts, singles sold, and most number one albums of any act.

- In the UK, The Beatles have 4 multi-platinum albums, 4 platinum albums, 8 gold albums, and 1 silver album.

- Between 1962 and 1970, the Lennon-McCartney partnership published around 180 jointly credited songs, of which most were for The Beatles. George Harrison wrote 22 songs, and Ringo Starr wrote 2 songs for the band. The remaining The Beatles songs were group collaborations.

CHAPTER 12:

SOLO CAREERS

TRIVIA TIME!

1. Which Beatles member was the first to release a non-soundtrack solo album?

   a. Paul McCartney
   b. George Harrison
   c. Ringo Starr
   d. John Lennon

2. What was the name of John Lennon's first post-Beatles project, which he started with his second wife, Yoko Ono?

   a. John and Yoko
   b. The Onos
   c. Plastic Ono Band
   d. The Band of John and Yoko

3. Recorded in secret and released in April of 1970, what was the name of Paul McCartney's debut solo album?

   a. *McCartney*
   b. *Fly*
   c. *Find My Way*

d. *Just Paul*

4. Released in 1971, what became John Lennon's best-selling single of his solo career after his murder?

   a. "Give Peace a Chance"
   b. "Imagine"
   c. "(Just Like) Starting Over"
   d. "#9 Dream"

5. With 43 platinum singles and over 100 million records sold globally, which Beatle has had the most successful solo career?

   a. John Lennon
   b. Paul McCartney
   c. George Harrison
   d. Ringo Starr

6. How many albums did John Lennon complete during his infamous "Lost Weekend" period?

   a. 0
   b. 3
   c. 7
   d. 9

7. True or False: After The Beatles dissolved, Ringo Starr played the drums on albums for Lennon, Harrison, and McCartney.

8. Released in 1970, what was the name of Ringo Starr's debut solo album?

   a. *Ringo's Starrs*
   b. *Starkey and the Rockstars*
   c. *Exploration*

d. *Sentimental Journey*

9. Which song did John Lennon record with Elton John that was Lennon's only number one single in the United States during his lifetime?

   a. "Whatever Gets You Thru the Night"
   b. "Lucy in the Sky with Diamonds"
   c. "I Saw Her Standing There"
   d. "Imagine"

10. Recorded with his solo band, which song was Ringo's first number one hit, a tune on which he collaborated with George Harrison?

    a. "You're Sixteen"
    b. "Photograph"
    c. "It Don't Come Easy"
    d. "Nevermind Without You"

11. What is the title of Paul McCartney's chart-topping song he recorded with Michael Jackson?

    a. "Hey Hey Hey"
    b. "Today Today Today"
    c. "Say Say Say"
    d. "Hurray Hurray Hurray"

12. George Harrison's debut solo album with which title was also the soundtrack to a 1968 film?

    a. *Wonderwall Music*
    b. *Chitty Chitty Bang Bang*
    c. *The Party*
    d. *Ice Station Zebra*

13. Formed in 1971, what was the original name of Paul

McCartney's band?

a. Feathers
b. Birds
c. Wings
d. Eagles

14. What is the name of Ringo's band (a rock supergroup of shifting personnel)?

a. Ringo and His Starrs
b. Ringo Starr & His All Starr Band
c. All Starr Ringo Band
d. Ringo Band All Starrs

15. True or False: Ringo Starr never made it as an actor.

16. In 1987, George Harrison formed his supergroup of five stellar musicians called what?

a. Boppin' Bards
b. Worldwide Rock
c. Jackaroos
d. The Traveling Wilburys

17. Which John Lennon song from his first post-Beatles album includes the lyrics "I don't believe in Beatles"?

a. "God"
b. "Mother"
c. "Well Well Well"
d. "Remember"

18. Which charity event, organized by Ravi Shankar and George Harrison (at Harrison's request), took place on August 1, 1971?

a. The Concert for Bangladesh

b. The Concert for the Hungry

c. The Concert for India

d. The Concert for the People

19. What was the title of George Harrison's first solo Billboard number one hit?

a. "Beware of Darkness"

b. "Let It Down"

c. "What is Life"

d. "My Sweet Lord"

20. What kind of therapy heavily influenced John Lennon's debut post-Beatles album, which was co-written with Yoko Ono?

a. Hypnotherapy

b. Primal Scream Therapy

c. Horticulture Therapy

d. Chess Therapy

ANSWERS

1. b — George Harrison

2. c — Plastic Ono Band

3. a — *McCartney*

4. b — "Imagine"

5. b — Paul McCartney

6. b — 3

7. True

8. d — *Sentimental Journey*

9. a — "Whatever Gets You Thru the Night"

10. b — "Photograph"

11. c — "Say Say Say"

12. a — *Wonderwall Music*

13. c — Wings

14. b — Ringo Starr and His All Starr Band

15. False

16. d — The Traveling Wilburys

17. a — "God"

18. a — The Concert for Bangladesh

19. d — "My Sweet Lord"

20. b — Primal Scream Therapy

DID YOU KNOW?

- Paul McCartney's band Wings was formed in 1971, featuring his wife Linda on keyboards, former Moody Blues guitarist Denny Laine, and session drummer Denny Seiwell. The band was active for about a decade, and their biggest Hot 100 hit was "Silly Love Songs" in 1976.

- Formed in 1989, Ringo Starr & His All Starr Band is a rock supergroup, meaning that the performers have their own successful careers as soloists and play in other bands or in a related profession. The band has toured consistently over the last three decades and rotates its line-up. They do not compose original music, with the exception of the song "Island in the Sun," which was off of Starr's 2015 album *Postcards from Paradise*.

- The Traveling Wilburys were George Harrison's supergroup band, consisting of Harrison, Bob Dylan, Jeff Lynne, Roy Orbison, and Tom Petty. While recording for his solo album *Cloud Nine* in 1987, Harrison and Lynne discussed the idea, and the band formed in April of 1988. The group's first album, *Traveling Wilburys Vol. 1*, won the Grammy for "Best Rock Performance by a Duo or Group" in 1990.

- After The Beatles broke up, Ringo continued to act in various films, some of which include *Candy* (1968), *The Magic Christian* (1969), *Blindman* (1971), *Son of Dracula* (1971), and *Caveman* (1981). He both starred and made cameos, and even voice acted for a few episodes of animated shows such as *The Simpsons* and *The Powderpuff Girls*.

- Paul McCartney reunited with George Martin for the James Bond theme song "Live and Let Die," written by Paul and Linda McCartney. Martin produced and arranged the orchestra, and the song became the first rock song used for a Bond film.

- The only member to not have a direct conflict with any of the three other Beatles, Ringo Starr continued to drum and collaborate with each of them on their solo albums.

- In 1972, John Lennon and Yoko Ono released a television-film along with the *Imagine* album. It was a home movie featuring footage of them in the home, garden, and recording studio of their Berkshire property, as well as in New York City. Several celebrities appear in the film, including Fred Astaire, Andy Warhol, Dick Cavett, Jack Palance, and fellow ex-Beatle George Harrison.

CHAPTER 13:

CULTURAL AND COMMERCIAL INFLUENCE

TRIVIA TIME!

1. In 1963, what was a collective term used to describe bands and singers from Liverpool?

   a. Liverpool Rock
   b. Merseybeat
   c. Northern Brits
   d. British Beat

2. Which of the following best describes what drew teenagers to The Beatles' attitude?

   a. Purity
   b. Obscenity
   c. Formality
   d. Informality

3. Attended by members of the royal family, what was the name of the televised show The Beatles played for in 1963?

   a. Royal Extravaganza

b. Royal Variety Performance

c. Royal Cabaret

d. Royal Talent Show

4. True or False: The Beatles' iconic hairstyle, while popular, was not imitated by American males, despite the "Beatlemania" sweeping the nation.

5. During The Beatles' 1964 World Tour, a crowd of 300,000 people, the biggest Beatle crowd ever, lined the streets of which Australian city to watch The Beatles' motorcade?

a. Adelaide

b. Sydney

c. Melbourne

d. Perth

6. As The Beatles emerged into international stardom, which part of their image was imitated as an act of rebellion?

a. Bell-bottom pants

b. Unbuttoned shirt

c. Long hair

d. All pink attire

7. To complement their new suit image, The Beatles commissioned four pairs of boots that are now a style called what?

a. The cactus boot

b. The Beatle boot

c. The punk boot

d. The go-go boot

8. True or False: Before The Beatles, British music groups had always been more popular than American groups.

9. Which cultural movement of the 1960s did The Beatles create that features revolution and evolution themes?

    a. Anticulture
    b. Expansionist Movement
    c. Counterculture
    d. Capitalist Movement

10. Which animated band released a tribute album singing The Beatles hits in 1964?

    a. Alvin and the Chipmunks
    b. The Archies
    c. The Nutty Squirrels
    d. The Beets

11. The Beatles embraced the religion of which country?

    a. China
    b. Britain
    c. Israel
    d. India

12. True or False: In the early 1960s, some British politicians used The Beatles to gain political advantages.

13. Which major tragic event had occurred in the US a few months before the arrival of The Beatles, making their upbeat attitudes, music, and performances a welcome change?

    a. The Vietnam War
    b. The assassination of John F. Kennedy
    c. The Manson Murders
    d. The assassination of Martin Luther King Jr.

14. Which of the following companies offered the purchase of

four inflatable, autographed The Beatles dolls on the label of their powdered product in 1964?

a. Nestle
b. McDonald's
c. Lipton
d. Quaker Oats

15. Which author and filmmaker was quoted as saying, "The Beatles are the only mere pop group you could remove from history and suggest that culturally, without them, things would have been significantly different"?

a. Ingmar Bergman
b. Hanif Kureishi
c. Michael Apted
d. Derek Jarman

16. True or False: The Beatles' international success was what first created an export market for British pop music.

17. Which accomplished social historian declared The Beatles' US breakthrough to be the "single critical event that established the hegemony of youth-inspired British popular culture"?

a. R.B. McCallum
b. Herbert Paul
c. Arthur Marwick
d. Asa Briggs

18. After The Beatles' success caused many to think of British culture as "the most exciting culture on Earth," which British city was recognized as the "Swinging City" of international culture?

a. Liverpool

b. London

c. Manchester

d. Cambridge

19. Which British weekly music magazine began a campaign for the Beatles to be awarded "The Most Excellent Order of the British Empire," or MBEs for short, due to their substantial contribution to the national economy?

a. BBC Music Magazine

b. Classic Rock

c. Jazz Journal

d. Melody Maker

ANSWERS

1. b – Merseybeat

2. d – Informality

3. b – Royal Variety Show

4. False

5. a – Adelaide

6. c – Long hair

7. b – The Beatle boot

8. False

9. c – Counterculture

10. a – Alvin and the Chipmunks

11. d – India

12. True

13. b – The assassination of John F. Kennedy

14. a – Nestle

15. b – Hanif Kureishi

16. True

17. c – Arthur Marwick

18. b – London

19. d – Melody Maker

20. False

DID YOU KNOW?

- In the early 1960's, wages and salaries increased, free time was becoming more abundant, and the demand for entertainment rose. People of working-class origin were able to become successful, and the youth were able to make money. Pop culture developed surrounding the youth of the time and became more commercialized to meet the demand for entertainment. In a lot of ways, The Beatles were in the right place at the right time.

- The Beatles ushered in the original golden age of British rock and roll, usurping the American acts and reversing the idea that British acts paled in comparison to American groups of the same style.

- Beatle boots are a combination of the Chelsea boot and the flamenco boot. They originated in 1961 when John Lennon and Paul McCartney commissioned four pairs of Chelsea boots with the addition of the Cuban heel. The boots were very popular with rock artists in the 1960s, including The Monkees, Roy Orbison, The Beach Boys, The Zombies, The Kinks, and Elvis Presley, to name a few.

- Seltaeb was a local subsidiary through Epstein's NEMS Enterprises through which The Beatles merchandise was marketed. There was The Beatles-themed wallpaper, jewelry, toys, clothing, stationery, alarm clocks, pillowcases, bath products, junk food, lunchboxes, wigs, and even The Beatles brand chewing gum.

- The Beatles revolutionized songwriting by combining the roles of songwriter and performer. They at least contributed, if not started, an era of self-contained rock bands. The band's experimental period added further developments to pop music in regards to modal mixture, extended form, huge chords, and the regular addition of the bridge in a song.

- Apple Corps was founded with the intention to be an alternative system of production in which artists would not have to conform to standard industry rules. Apple Records was unique in that it was an artist-run label from which the band members could further their own interests and support other artists.

- The Beatles are viewed as representing the ideals of the 1960s as iconic images of the decade. They are timeless, and continue to accumulate fans, particularly among today's youth, 50 years post-breakup.

- The lyrics, music, appearance, and ideas of The Beatles were constantly evolving and changing with the environment around them. They never grew boring and stayed relevant and innovative.

- Unfortunately, The Beatles' US success had a negative effect on many singers and songwriters that the band members themselves admired. Those with similar styles of music found themselves making much less money than before, and some even found themselves completely ousted from the entertainment business. However, in the long run, the Beatles helped many of their influence achieve greater global recognition.

- When The Beatles received their "Most Excellent Order of

the British Empire" awards from Queen Elizabeth II herself, they set a precedent for the country's entertainers to be given similar awards in the following decades.

- The Beatles' mop-top haircuts made them appear less threatening to teenage girls, while their suits helped them seem less "sleazy" than Elvis Presley to the middle-class.

- Those mop-top haircuts were a spectacle at the time, given that crew cuts were the previous norm. It became such a popular image that "The Beatles wigs" were sold.

CHAPTER 14:

INSPIRATIONS

TRIVIA TIME!

1. Which Beach Boys' album was inspired by The Beatles album *Rubber Soul*?

   a. *Pet Sounds*
   b. *Beach Boys' Party!*
   c. *All Summer Long*
   d. *The Beach Boys Today!*

2. Reflecting on one of the pioneers of rock and roll music, John Lennon said, "If you had to give rock and roll another name, you might call it —" what?

   a. Elvis Presley
   b. Chuck Berry
   c. Little Richard
   d. Fats Domino

3. True or False: *Sgt. Pepper's Lonely Hearts Club Band* was inspired by The Beach Boys' album *Smiley Smile*.

4. Which Beach Boys song has Paul McCartney cited as his

favorite song of all time?

a. "Wouldn't It Be Nice"
b. "I Get Around"
c. "God Only Knows"
d. "Good Vibrations"

5. True or False: Former Black Sabbath frontman Ozzy Osbourne has said that he owes his whole career to The Beatles.

6. Which American country-inspired rock and roll duo's sound heavily influenced The Beatles' early pop songs such as "Love Me Do" and "Please Please Me"?

a. The Righteous Brothers
b. The Everly Brothers
c. Ike and Tina Turner
d. Simon and Garfunkel

7. Which famous rock and roll artist were The Beatles excited to meet after receiving an invitation to his home in Beverly Hills in 1965?

a. Elvis Presley
b. Frank Sinatra
c. Chuck Berry
d. Jimmy Page

8. True or False: David Bowie's favorite Beatle was Paul McCartney.

9. Established in 1964 and widely regarded as 'The American Beatles," which rock band's sound was initially very similar to The Beatles, earning them that moniker?

a. The Eagles

b. The Beach Boys

c. The Bee Gees

d. The Byrds

10. When reflecting on The Beatles' performance on *The Ed Sullivan Show*, which famous 1970s rock band lead singer and bassist has admitted to being "a child of The Beatles"?

a. Lou Reed

b. Van Halen

c. Gene Simmons

d. Robert Plant

11. Nirvana's music seemed to have been influenced by The Beatles as a whole. However, which individual Beatle was known to be Kurt Cobain's favorite?

a. Ringo Starr

b. John Lennon

c. George Harrison

d. Paul McCartney

12. True or False: Initially, The Monkees and The Beatles were serious rivals, publicly shaming each other for ripping off each other's music.

13. Often compared to The Beatles, which band rose to fame in the 1990s and was transparent about drawing their influence from them, along with lyrical references to The Beatles songs?

a. Pearl Jam

b. Oasis

c. Weezer

d. Red Hot Chili Peppers

14. Released under the pseudonym Bonnie Jo Mason, what was the name of Cher's 1965 promotional single that was a tribute to The Beatles?

    a. "Paul, I Love You"
    b. "John, I Love You"
    c. "George, I Love You"
    d. "Ringo, I Love You"

15. What is the name of the Flaming Lips track-for-track tribute album of *Sgt. Pepper's Lonely Hearts Club Band*?

    a. *Sgt. Pepper's Wonely Hearts Club Band*
    b. *All You Need is Wove*
    c. *With a Little Help From My Fwends*
    d. *Wucy in the Sky with Diamonds*

16. True or False: Lady Gaga has stated that when she wrote her album *The Fame*, she listened to The Beatles' *Abbey Road* obsessively.

ANSWERS

1. a—*Pet Sounds*

2. b—Chuck Berry

3. False

4. c—"God Only Knows"

5. True

6. b—The Everly Brothers

7. a—Elvis Presley

8. False

9. d—The Byrds

10. c—Gene Simmons

11. b—John Lennon

12. False

13. b—Oasis

14. d—Ringo, I Love You

15. c—*With a Little Help From My Fwends*

16. True

DID YOU KNOW?

- Little Richard, Fats Domino, Buddy Holly, Elvis Presley, and Chuck Berry were all influential to the beginnings of The Beatles as a rock band. They covered many of their songs, especially in the beginning, including "Roll Over Beethoven," "Long Tall Sally," and "Johnny B. Goode." Fats Domino's song "Ain't That a Shame" is noted as the first song John Lennon learned to play.

- The Byrds, Creedence Clearwater Revival, Billy Joel, Nancy Wilson from Heart, and Joe Walsh from The Eagles are said to have been inspired to start their musical careers after watching The Beatles on *The Ed Sullivan Show*.

- Elvis Presley was one of the biggest influences on rock and roll artists of the UK at the time. Before The Beatles were even a band, John Lennon and Paul McCartney recalled when Elvis entered the British charts and ignited their love for rock and roll music. According to The Beatles historian Mark Lewisohn, The Beatles/The Quarrymen performed over 30 Elvis songs during their live shows.

- When speaking to the End The Silence Campaign by the charity Hope and Homes For Children, Ozzy chose The Beatles song "She Loves You" as the song that made a difference in his life when he was younger. He went on to say, "I remember exactly where I was. I was walking down Witton Road in Aston, I had a blue transistor radio and when that song came on, I knew from then on what I wanted to do with my life. This was so brand new, and it gave me a great feeling. Then I became an avid Beatles fan—they were great. I owe my career to them because they gave me the desire to want to be in the music game."

- Although David Bowie admired all of The Beatles and their music, he was closest with John Lennon. They even co-wrote one of Bowie's most successful singles "Fame."

- The Monkees were initially selected and marketed as American television's response to The Beatles. After the show ended, the band continued to improve their skills and make music, even becoming a self-directed band. While the media would speculate they "ripped off" The Beatles, the Fab Four were actually good friends with the four Monkees.

- "The American Beatles" has been a title thrown around in reference to a few different groups, with The Byrds being the most widely recognized usage. It was their early folk rock music that was inspired by The Beatles, but they were distinguishably not imitators.

CHAPTER 15:

ODDS AND ENDS

TRIVIA TIME!

1. True or False: Apple Inc., the creator of the iPhone, bought the rights to the name from The Beatles.

2. Which song by The Beatles used a take in which they started playing while Ringo Starr was in the restroom, returning just in time for his own part?

    a. "Let It Be"
    b. "Something"
    c. "Hey Jude"
    d. "I Am the Walrus"

3. What was the name of John Lennon's sound collage released by The Beatles in late 1968?

    a. "Revolution 9"
    b. "Liverpool Sound Collage"
    c. "Don't Worry Kyoko"
    d. "Golden Slumbers"

4. True or False: The Beatles were the first pop group to be

represented as wax figures in Madame Tussaud's museum.

5. Which US President was at odds with John Lennon, pushing for his deportation in order to secure his reelection?

    a. John F. Kennedy
    b. Lyndon B. Johnson
    c. Richard Nixon
    d. Gerald Ford

6. Based on his roots in England and his last name, what is Paul McCartney's well-known nickname?

    a. Mac
    b. Macca
    c. Mick
    d. Carter

7. True or False: Paul McCartney's full name is James Paul McCartney.

8. What was the name of the video game released in 2009 featuring The Beatles?

    a. The Beatles: The Game
    b. The Beatles: Experience
    c. The Beatles: Rock Band
    d. The Beatles: Play Like a Rockstar

9. Approximately how long did The Beatles play at a typical concert?

    a. 30 minutes
    b. 60 minutes
    c. 90 minutes
    d. 120 minutes

10. True or False: The Beatles song "I Am the Walrus" has

layers of underlying meaning in its lyrics.

11. Which of the following musicians purchased John Lennon's upright Steinway Model Z piano in 2000 and toured globally with it before placing it on display at Strawberry Field as the "Imagine Piano"?

    a. Yoko Ono
    b. Paul McCartney
    c. Cynthia Lennon
    d. George Michael

12. Which Beatles song, penned by John Lennon, was beamed into space by NASA in 2008 to celebrate the 50th anniversary of NASA's founding and the 40th anniversary of the song itself?

    a. "Strawberry Fields Forever"
    b. "Sun King"
    c. "Lucy in the Sky with Diamonds"
    d. "Across the Universe"

13. John Lennon purchased his first guitar in 1956. Who lent him the five pounds and ten shillings to do so?

    a. His Uncle George
    b. His mother, Julia
    c. His Aunt Mimi
    d. His cousin Stanley

14. True or False: At some point, all of The Beatles have been vegetarians, and the two surviving members have continued to be vegetarians.

15. What was the name of Paul McCartney's 1984 musical drama film that starred him, Ringo Starr, and Bryan

Brown?

a. *Wingspan*
b. *Movin' On*
c. *Give My Regards to Broad Street*
d. *Put It There*

16. True or False: The Beatles were never sued for plagiarism because all of their music content was original.

17. Two years before joining the band that would become The Beatles, George Harrison formed his own skiffle group called which of the following?

a. The Riot
b. The Rebels
c. The Fighters
d. The Renegades

18. In 2008, a topiary tribute to The Beatles was unveiled in Liverpool, one of which was vandalized shortly after. It's believed that the vandal targeted this Beatle since he had once stated he "missed nothing" about the city. Which topiary Beatle was beheaded?

a. Ringo Starr
b. George Harrison
c. Paul McCartney
d. John Lennon

19. In *Rolling Stone* magazine's list of the "100 Greatest Guitarists of All Time," what was George Harrison's rank?

a. 1st
b. 7th
c. 11th

d. 24th

ANSWERS

1. True

2. c — "Hey Jude"

3. a — "Revolution 9"

4. True

5. c — Richard Nixon

6. b — Macca

7. True

8. c — The Beatles: Rock Band

9. a — 30 minutes

10. False

11. d — George Michael

12. d — "Across the Universe"

13. b — His mother, Julia

14. True

15. c — *Give My Regards to Broad Street*

16. False

17. b — The Rebels

18. a — Ringo Starr

19. c — 11th

DID YOU KNOW?

- "Revolution 9" is the longest track of The Beatles' career. It appeared on The Beatles' self-titled album (also known as *The White Album*) and was created primarily by John Lennon with assistance from George Harrison and Yoko Ono. Lennon had the idea to paint a picture of revolution using sound, combining numerous overdubbed vocals, speech, tape loops, performances, sound effects manipulated with echo, reversals, distortion, fading, and stereo panning. It began as an extended ending to Lennon's song "Revolution."

- It is well-known that John Lennon publicly advocated for peace and was against the Vietnam War in the '70s. 1972 was the first year that 18-year-olds could vote in the US, and Lennon had plans to mobilize the new youth vote against Nixon's administration by following his campaign stops as a tour, ending in Miami at the time of the Republican National Convention. Concerned Lennon could affect his chances at reelection, President Richard Nixon had the FBI observe him and force him into a deportation fight with the government. They succeeded in pressuring Lennon to cancel his plans, but Lennon was never deported.

- In 1999, Harrison was stabbed in the chest repeatedly when he and his wife were attacked by a crazed man in their home. He suffered multiple stab wounds and a collapsed lung but luckily survived the attack.

- The Beatles were accused of plagiarism on several occasions, and they were even sued in court a few times. Two mentionable instances are with the songs "Come Together" and "My Sweet Lord." Being heavily influenced by Chuck Berry, Lennon's "Come Together" sounded much like "You Can't Catch Me" and quoted Berry with the lyrics "Here comes old flat-top." The clear antecedent to Harrison's "My Sweet Lord" was "He's So Fine" by The Chiffons. In both cases, fault was admitted, and the cases were settled.

- Ringo Starr was quite sick as a child, as he spent nearly half his early life in and out of hospitals, recovering from one illness or another. In his early teen years, while staying at a sanatorium during one of these long stints of recovery time, Ringo was first introduced to percussion as a result of his joining the hospital band, where his first "instrument" was a makeshift mallet, made from a cotton bobbin, which he used to strike cabinets near his bed.

- John Lennon's first guitar was a Gallotone Champion, an acoustic that was cheaply made in South Africa and exported to many other countries. Despite its low cost to make, after Lennon's death, the instrument was sold at a "Rock'nRoll" memorabilia sale by Sotheby's London for $224,000.

CHAPTER 16:

THE BEATLES NOW

TRIVIA TIME!

1. Which Beatle has the highest net worth?

   a. George Harrison
   b. Ringo Starr
   c. John Lennon
   d. Paul McCartney

2. Released on December 18, 2020, what is the name of Paul McCartney's 18th solo album?

   a. *McCartney III*
   b. *Flaming Pie*
   c. *Egypt Station*
   d. *McCartney II*

3. To be released in 2021, what is the title of the highly anticipated documentary from director Peter Jackson?

   a. *Let It Be: Uncut*
   b. *The Beatles: Get Back*
   c. *The Beatles: Rare Footage*

d. *Before Abbey Road*

4. What is the name of the single penned by Dianne Warren, which Ringo Starr released on December 18, 2020?

   a. "Here's to the Nights"
   b. "Raise Your Glass"
   c. "Thank God for Music"
   d. "Times Like This"

5. At 58 years old, in which year did George Harrison pass away after a lengthy battle with cancer?

   a. 1999
   b. 2000
   c. 2001
   d. 2002

6. John Lennon is survived by two sons, one from each of his marriages. What is the name of his son with Yoko Ono?

   a. Julian Lennon
   b. Sean Lennon
   c. Jack Lennon
   d. Kyoko Lennon

7. True or False: Yoko Ono has attended every parole hearing for Mark David Chapman.

8. Which honor did George Harrison receive posthumously in 2015?

   a. The Nobel Peace Prize
   b. Billboard Music Century Award
   c. Grammy for Album of the Year
   d. The Grammys Lifetime Achievement Award

9. What is the name of the album released on John Lennon's

80th birthday in 2020?

a. *Imagine, Reimagined*
b. *Gimme Some Truth. The Ultimate Mixes*
c. *Love One Another*
d. *The Roots of John Lennon*

10. Originally set to open in late 2020, Paul McCartney is a writer for the musical adaptation of which classic Christmas film?

a. *It's a Wonderful Life*
b. *Miracle on 34th Street*
c. *White Christmas*
d. *A Christmas Story*

11. True or False: Both Ringo Starr and Paul McCartney had tours scheduled in 2020 that had to be postponed.

12. Announced in early 2021, who is to direct the documentary film about Abbey Road Studios titled *If These Walls Could Sing*?

a. Mary McCartney
b. Stella McCartney
c. James McCartney
d. Heather McCartney

13. How many kids does Paul McCartney have?

a. 2
b. 3
c. 5
d. 8

14. True or False: Both of Ringo Starr's sons are drummers.

15. A well-known name in the world of fashion, who is Paul

and Linda McCartney's most famous child?

a. Mary McCartney
b. Beatrice McCartney
c. Stella McCartney
d. James McCartney

16. Who is George and Olivia Harrison's only child?

a. Ishaan Harrison
b. Kavan Harrison
c. Tejas Harrison
d. Dhani Harrison

17. True or False: Along with K-pop band BTS, The Beatles were the top-selling band of 2020 as one of the only two groups to sell over 1 million units.

18. Cynthia and Julian Lennon unveiled which of the following on the day of John Lennon's 70th birthday in 2010 at Chavasse Park, Liverpool?

a. The Memorial of Peace
b. The John Lennon Peace Monument
c. John Lennon's Strawberry Fields
d. John Lennon's Peaceful Garden

19. Which charity did George Harrison found in 1973, often abbreviated as MWF?

a. The Make a Wish Foundation
b. The Material World Charitable Foundation
c. The Magic Wholesome Foundation
d. The Mr. Whirly Foundation

ANSWERS

1. d — Paul McCartney

2. a — McCartney III

3. b — *The Beatles: Get Back*

4. False

5. a — "Here's to the Nights"

6. c — 2001

7. b — Sean Lennon

8. False

9. d — The Grammys Lifetime Achievement Award

10. b — *Gimme Some Truth. The Ultimate Mixes*

11. a — *It's a Wonderful Life*

12. True

13. a — Mary McCartney

14. c — 5

15. True

16. c — Stella McCartney

17. d — Dhani Harrison

18. True

19. b — The John Lennon Peace Monument

20. b — The Material World Charitable Foundation

DID YOU KNOW?

- Although John Lennon passed away in 1980, his legacy has lived on through his music, family, and fans. To this day, his life, music, and activism are regularly commemorated and have continued to inspire. Starting in 1997, Yoko Ono and the BMI Foundation established an annual music competition program for contemporary songwriters called the *John Lennon Scholarships*. In 2002, the airport in John Lennon's hometown was renamed the *Liverpool John Lennon Airport*.

- Keeping a largely successful solo career, Ringo Starr has continued to release new music and tour when possible. In celebration of his 80th birthday in July of 2020, Ringo organized a live-stream concert collaborating with McCartney, Walks, Ben Harper, Sheryl Crow, Dave Grohl, Sheila E., and Willie Nelson. Slated for release on March 19, 2021, Ringo's newest album titled *Zoom In* includes the lead single "Here's to the Night."

- Paul McCartney has gone on to enjoy a very successful career as one of the most successful composers and performers of all time. Current projects include *High in the Clouds* (an animation project for Netflix, based on McCartney's children's adventure novel), a special reissue of *Flaming Pie* (10th solo studio album), and a 50th anniversary limited-edition release of *McCartney*, his first solo album.

Now that you have finished reading *The Beatles – History and Trivia*, you are hopefully left with a deeper connection and a more thorough understanding of one of the greatest bands in the history of music. We look forward to seeing what projects, music, and memories continue to unfold in the coming years!

Printed in Great Britain
by Amazon

80136738R00078